ALAN HAUGHTON

RHYTHM AND

16 PIECES IN VARIOUS POPULAR STYLES

THE ASSOCIATED BOARD OF
THE ROYAL SCHOOLS OF MUSIC

INTRODUCTION

Alan Haughton studied pianoforte at the Royal Academy of Music from 1968 to 1971 with Leslie England and Max Pirani. He won the Eric Brough Memorial Prize and was awarded the L.R.A.M. Diploma. Whilst studying at the Academy he became interested in jazz and the various piano styles encompassed by this form. *Rhythm and Rag* reflects this interest.

Alan Haughton is Deputy Headteacher of a Lower School in Bedfordshire. He has been involved in music education since 1975 and is particularly aware of the need for music which gives young musicians a contemporary starting point.

For Isabel Beyer and Harvey Dagul

RHYTHM AND RAG

FREEWAY

ALAN HAUGHTON

BOOGIE ON DOWN

rit.
a tempo
p
mf
simile
f
rit.
f allarg.
p
P
WAGONTRAIN BLUES
Moderato (♩ = c.108)
3
f
p
Rolling along
p

f
p
f
p
rit.
mf
P

BLUE NOTE

LAZY

scherz. mf
sempre stacc.
f
p
p
rall.
legato
pp

CAROLYN'S SONG

GOING HOME

fp
sf
p
R.H.
R.H.
f
fz

ON THE RUN

Allegro vivace ($\text{half note} = 116$)

p
pp
rit.
L.H.
f
a tempo
mp
p veloce
8
accel.
morendo
pp

TOCCATA

Tails up: R.H.   Tails down: L.H.

STEPHANIE'S SONG

rall.
R.H.

FANFARE

Grandioso (♩ = 160)
11
ff
simile
P
p
ff
p dolce
L.H.
molto cresc.
ff
simile

p dolce
lusingando
smorz.
ppp

EVENING SONG

★ The title refers to the two dimensions of A major and A♭ major

Tempo I
mp
mf
rit.
Tempo I
mf
f

ALL ALONE

RAINY DAY RAG

cantabile
poco a poco cresc.
meno mosso

YOU AND ME

Printed by
Halstan & Co. Ltd., Amersham, Bucks., England

10/00